Mary Doward Lloyd

AUNT ABBY'S
NEIGHBORS

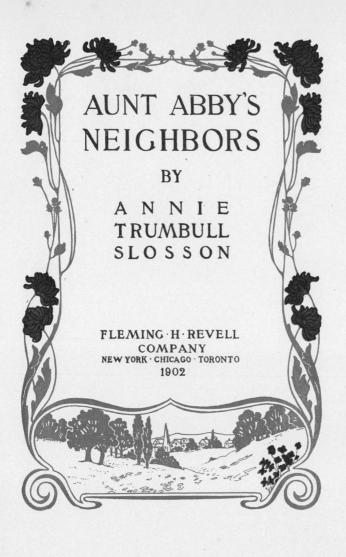

AUNT ABBY'S NEIGHBORS

BY

A N N I E
TRUMBULL
S L O S S O N

FLEMING · H · REVELL
COMPANY
NEW YORK · CHICAGO · TORONTO
1902

CONTENTS

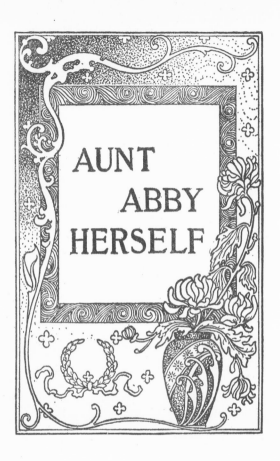

AUNT
ABBY
HERSELF

I AUNT
ABBY HERSELF

YES, I was one of Abby Coles's neighbors, her that everybody called Aunt Abby, you know. I am Rebecca Owen, and I lived next door to her a long spell in Factoryville and when she moved here I followed, some months afterwards, and was right across the street from her house all the rest of the time till she went away from us. I mean to be close to her, when my time comes, in the burying ground there across the river, and I hope I won't be very far away from her mansion up above, in that quiet, beautiful neighborhood she was always thinking about and often speaking of.

" I suppose there 's nobody living now that was a neighbor of hers so long as me. And that's the principal reason I've consented to tell you about her, though there's many and many other people that knew her who could tell it in better words. Another reason is that I took down some of her talks and have them all written out as near as can be in her own words. That may seem sort of queer to you, but it was this way. My father was a great hand for keeping account of things; it seemed to come natural to him. He kept lots and lots of blank books and wrote down what he called his records in them. He had one for the weather and could tell you out of it just how the wind was on such a day ten years before, whether it was wet or dry, droughty or falling weather.

"Another book was about the deaths and births and marriages in the town, and another about the crops and gardens. And there was one about the people and their doings and sayings, and—oh, I don't know what all. And I kind of took that taste from him and had my own little books full of records. And when I came to know Abby Coles—it was pretty late in her life I first became acquainted with her—and I saw what she was and how good and helpful and appropriate her talks were, why I begun writing them down.

"Of course I didn't let her know I

was doing it; it might have made
her talk a little stiffer, not so easy
and plain and natural if she felt
somebody was going to write it off.
And she never set anything by her
own talks, not a mite. She was
dreadful humble, and I've heard
her time and time again say, ' My !
how much good I might have done
in this world if I'd only had book
learning and knew how to put things
so's to interest folks, learn them the
truth, help them, strengthen them,
chirk them up. Paul had that, you
know, but he said himself that lots
of folks didn't, that there was all
kinds of gifts, prophesying and
working miracles and all, but not
everybody had what he called the
gift of tongues but what we plain
folks here call the " gift of gab," the

right kind of gab, you know.' Hers
was the right kind, the blessedest
kind of gab I tell you. I've got a
good memory, just as father had,
and after I'd heard Aunt Abby talk
on these occasions, I'd go home and
put it down on paper right off, just
as she had said it. And if I disre-
membered any part of it I'd sort of
lead her back to the subject next
time I saw her and that way I'd re-
fresh my mind and get so I could
recollect the whole thing.

" As for describing her, picturing
her out just as she was, telling you
how it was she did so much good,
helped folks so, and is remembered
and set store by to this day as nobody else I ever knew was, why
that's a hard thing to do, not pos-
sible it seems to me. I, for my part,

can't begin to do it and I don't think anybody can. And yet there wasn't anything very wonderful or surprising about her looks or her ways. She was sort of undersize, a short woman and kind of thin and she always dressed real plain, though as neat as a pin.

" When I knew her her hair was turning gray and she wore a cap. It's queer that well as I was acquainted with her I can't tell you what color her eyes were. But I can see them at this very minute as plain as if I were looking into them. But the look in them, the loving wanting-to-help, feeling-with-you look, why that just covered up the color or made you forget all about it. I never saw such eyes; they just drew you right close up to her, softened

you, mellowed you, and yet sort of
gave you strength and help too.
But you can't understand; you
never knew Aunt Abby Coles.

" If I was asked what was the most
stand-out, rememberable thing about
her why I should say just what anybody else that ever knew her would
say, 'twas her interest in her neighbors. Now I don't mean her spying
on them, finding out about their
own affairs, preaching at them, gossiping about them or anything like
that. I mean her real interest in
them and all that happened to them
in sorrow or in joy, her feeling with
them and for them and above all
wanting from the bottom of her
heart their real, best good, wishing
for it, praying for it and doing all
she could in her own quiet, pleasant

way to bring it about. She never meddled or pushed herself in where she wasn't wanted. So she never offended folks whatever she might talk to them about. And yet she wasn't all things to all men by any means. Some folks called it tact she had, but I don't think that's just the word to use. It was her *feeling with* people that did it all, not just feeling for but feeling with them and so knowing just what would or wouldn't hurt or vex them. ' It's real cheap and easy to feel *for* folks,' she used to say, ' and when you've done that or thought you have, why you feel comfortable and set-up and think you've done all that could be expected of you. But to feel *with* your neighbors that's hard ; it hurts. But it's the only way to help folks, and as I look back I see that's why I've failed so in every duty to my neighbors.'

" She wasn't just talking for effect when she ran herself down that way ; she really conceited that, as a neighbor she hadn't been a success. For you see the pattern she set up to try and copy was so dreadful high and difficult she felt she hadn't come nigh it. As for her own life it was a very plain, simple kind of life. She was always busy but never fussed. She moved about in a sort of still, easy but quick way and so got through a wonderful lot of work without ever seeming to be hurrying. And she always had time, plenty of time for anybody that needed her, but not a bit of leisure for idle, gossiping talk. As I said before there wasn't anything real striking or out of the common about her or her ways and so it's hard to make you see why it is that she and her quiet, plain, every-day life stands out to every one of us that knew her as something set on a hill that cannot be hid, as a light that shone before men so that they can never forget how bright and comforting it was.

"Another thing, she was a real Christian if ever there was one, but —I hope you won't misunderstand me—she didn't appear to pay much attention to her own Christian life. I mean she didn't cultivate what's called self-examination, and meditation on different subjects at stated times as is recommended, you know, in the books. You see she hadn't time. I've heard her say so myself

and she seemed sorry that 'twas so.
She'd say sometimes that it must be
real nice to shut yourself away from
everybody and all their troubles and
worries and think of yourself and
your own soul and of Him and of
heaven. 'But dear me!' she'd add,
'that's what you might call a
luxury and I can't afford it. I
haven't time, with so many neighbors and all their troubles and cares
to think of. Why, I've scarcely time
to pray for myself. I'm most
ashamed to tell you that some nights
when I say amen and start to get up
off my knees I recollect I haven't
said a word about myself, much as I
need His help, and it hadn't been a
short prayer, neither.'

"No, I tell you her prayers were
not short nor few. She didn't stand

at the corner of the streets nor make
' vain repetitions ' as the Bible says.
But I couldn't help hearing and seeing her, and though I didn't listen I
could hear the names of neighbor
after neighbor slip out, and know the
kind of things she was asking. The
light in her bedroom window burned
late most nights and I tell you 'twas
a dreadful comfort to look out at it
before we went to sleep and know
somebody was asking the best of
things for us, somebody that had a
good deal of influence too—though I
mean to say that with reverence.
That was the thing we missed most,
I guess, when that little light went
out. It was dark and lonesome and
seemed to throw a big responsibility
on each one of us, the having to
pray for ourselves more now that

she wasn't laying our wants before the Lord every day and night. But I think she'll find some way to let Him know what we, her old neighbors need.

"The light went out some years ago. She died just as she'd lived, quietlike and easy. She took cold watching with old Peter Binks, a colored man at the poorhouse, and it settled on her lungs. She was only sick a few days. There wasn't anything remarkable or striking about her last hours, no wonderful deathbed sayings and affecting last words. Even then, when you might think she had a right to a little rest and thinking about herself and her future, she had her neighbors on her mind to the last. Mr. Bates, her own minister, —she was a Congregationalist—

wasn't very well just then and she wouldn't have him sent for. She said Elder Slade, the Baptist, would come, she knew. So they brought him. But when he tried to ask her some questions about her state of mind and whether it was all peace with her and so on, in his kind, feeling way, she said, ' Please don't be mad, Elder, but I've got so little time left, you may skip all that. I guess it'll be all right; if it isn't it's my own fault, and there's so much to do now.' Then she went on with her weak, tired voice which couldn't much more than whisper and that real slow, telling him about this and that neighbor, their needs and their dangers, yes, to the very last. She spoke about little Billy Holmes's throat and how she hadn't quite finished the comforter she was knitting for him to wear cold days. She 'guessed some neighbor 'd bind it off and put tossells on the ends, for she'd promised there should be tossells and Billy mustn't go without his comforter.' Poor little fellow, he had to go without a comforter when she had gone away, but it wasn't very long. And she asked the Elder to call on Joel Fellows, 'not a past'ral call,' she says, 'that would scare him off, but a neighborly visit without any praying the first time. Let him down easy, Elder,' she whispers, 'and he'll come out all right.'

"And then she asked him to remind Mr. Bates, her own minister, what she'd said to him the other day about Cap'n Hyde, not for the world to bring in anything about falling from grace or the perseverance of the saints when they were talking together. ' His head's terrible troubled about those things,' she says, ' and there's lots of pleasanter and safer topics.' And so one after another she went over her neighbors and their wants to the last breath.

" For when we thought she had gone forever, the loving eyes shut up, and the pale hands laying still on her breast, all of a sudden we saw her white lips move a little and I put my ear close down to her face and I heard her say, ' And Mary— Wells—is—real—sorry—and—' She never finished, but we all understood and forgave poor wicked Mary Wells that minute for the sake of her that

asked us and came back, I really believe from the gate of heaven itself
to do it.

"It was a simple, quiet funeral as
she would have wanted it to be.
There was nobody there but her
neighbors, but every one in the village attended and many from other
places. For we had all learned to
use that word, neighbor, in her wide
meaning, which after all is the Bible
meaning too, though we mostly forget it."

AUNT ABBY
On
SECTS

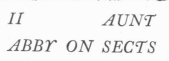

II AUNT ABBY ON SECTS

YES, I believe they do call me a mite lax in religious matters, — church matters, I would say. Only last week Miss Butler told me to my face I was time-serving and all things to all men. And Deacon Walker—my! he gave me up a long spell back as lukewarm and what he calls undenominational. That's a dreadful sounding word,— isn't it?

Well, mebbe I don't know myself, but seems to me I ain't time-serving, nor lukewarm, nor all things to all men, though I dare say I may be sort of the other thing, undenomi-

national. I'm a Congregational myself,—a " Congo," as we call it about
here, you know, for short. But
that's nothing to my credit nor my
discredit. I hadn't anything to say
about it. My folks were Congregationals, and so, as you might say, I
was born one. At any rate, I was
raised one by pa and ma. Well, as
long as I am one, elected to it, as you
might say, I'm going to be a good
one,—a strong one. There's no harm
in that. But I am *not* going to think
that folks of every other denomination are deluded, not to say wicked,
creatures. If that's what they call
undenominational, why, I'm it.

But I believe in sects, or denominations, whichever you may call
them. The way we're made, we
human creatures, they're really nec-

essary, seems to me. There's so many kinds of us, you see, with so many sorts of ways and tempers and feelings and natures, we've just got to go different ways, different roads. But, deary me! as long as all those roads bring up to the same place at the end, what kind of matter is it which folks take? And it keeps up interest to have these different societies with different ways to them, each one of the company belonging to them thinking his folks' way the best, and working zealous for his own sect. I believe 'twas so, way back from the beginning, when the apostles and their followers started the churches. I don't conceit that when the vision appeared that time to John on the island, and sent word to the churches by him, I don't believe that all those seven societies were run just exactly similar. Why, the way the messages read shows they were as different from each other as the denominations are nowadays. Ephesus church had its own way of doing things, and Smyrny had another ; Pergamos learnt its members one set of rules, and Sardis learnt different ones, and so through the whole seven. But they were all under one spiritual head, and took their orders from the One that sent them that time through John.

I'll go a little further, though this time I don't expect many folks to agree with me. It's my own idea, one of those things that appear to come into my head of themselves, as far as I know, and come to stay. This is it. I sort of believe there'll be dif-

ferent churches, or societies, or com-
panies, whatever you may call them,
up in heaven. You needn't look so
scared, that isn't as bad as it sounds.
They won't be run just as they are
down here, and there won't be so
much—well, friction's a good word,
mebbe, not to use a stronger one.
Somehow, to me it's a real comfortable, nice idea, the folks of the different organizations, that used to
hold by each other, and love their
own church so, with its own ways,
down below on the earth, their meeting, once in a while, at any rate, all
by themselves up there, and talking
about the old days; yes, even mebbe
singing some of the old hymns.
There are many mansions up there,
you know, and there are twelve different gates to go in by. And there

are all manner of different stones in the foundation, but every one of them's precious.

So you see I'm as denominational and sectarian as anybody in the world. But I know what people mean, and why they call me lax, and lukewarm, and all, and I'll tell you. As I said before, I was born and raised a Congregational. Now, when I was young, I really thought that was the only right and Christian sect, and all the others—Baptists, Methodists, Episcopals, Presbyterians, and all—were mistaken, deceived beings. You know how it is with young folks. To them there's one straight, even line running along; one side of it—that's their side, and their folks's—is the right side, and the other—that's other people's—is the wrong, and to them there's nothing betwixt or between. That's the way with these young, unknowing creatures in politics, religion, and everything.

There was a little girl that went to school with me, a great crony of mine, Fanny Mary Shaw. Now her folks were Baptists, and every night when I said my prayers, kneeling before the trundle-bed in Aunt Patty's room, I used to put in a request about Fanny Mary, and ask that she might be converted, meaning become a Congregational. Poor little Fanny Mary! She's been dead forty year, and I'd be satisfied to be received into the same mansion her Master prepared for her. And so 'twas with other sects; I didn't wish them any harm, but I pitied them

dreadfully, and prayed and hoped
they might reform. I had most
hopes for the Presbyterians, hearing
that they were nearest like the Congos. But still I thought even they
were running a terrible risk.

Well, the change in me about this
didn't come all at once. One lesson
at a time was learnt me, till, before I
really knew what was coming, I had
it all by heart, and looked on each
one of these organizations as close
relations of my own society, and
learned to love them all. But, as I
said before and say again, I like my
own best.

The first lesson I got was in a
hard time, and 'twas one of the
hardest to learn. For it was about
the Episcopals. Now from the way
I'd been brought up, that denomina-

tion had always seemed to me the most mistaken of any of them. Pa was one of the strict, old-fashioned sort, and he was dreadful set against the Episcopals. He thought they were all for forms, and not much for the spirit; said they didn't make up their own prayers, but read them out of books; that they wore strange, popish kind of clothes, and—oh! a lot of things. And I'd sort of taken it all in, as young folks will, and never looked into the subject myself. Well, there came a great sorrow into my life; my mother lay dying. 'Twas in the summer, and our minister was off on his vacation. So was the Baptist, and there was only those two churches in the village. But there was a boarder at Mrs. Lamson's that time,—a minister, an

Episcopal. I'd seen him time and
again go by the house in his queer,
straight-up-and-down coat, and Rom-
ish-looking vest and collar, and
every drop of pa's Protestant blood
in me had risen up against him. To
be sure, his face was kind and
his ways friendly, and he was real
pleasant spoken. But he was one of
that mistaken denomination, and
looked it, and I disapproved of him.

But what was I going to do
now? I couldn't let ma die without
a minister to pray with her,—I just
couldn't. Mrs. Lamson came over
to see me; she was a Congo herself,
and knew just how I felt. "But,"
says she, "he's a real good man, if he
is an Episcopal. Mebbe he's only
been that way a little spell, and isn't
a very strong one yet. Anyway,

he's good; I know that from lots of
little things, and he's a minister, and
there ain't another one handy."
"But oh!" I says, "suppose he
should *read* a prayer to her! Seems
's if pa's spirit would come back to
prevent that." "Mebbe he won't,"
says Mrs. Lamson. So I let her
speak to him, and he came over
right straight off.

Ma was pretty near the end,
feeble and helpless like, and sort of
drowsing most of the time. But
when Mr. Palmer—that was his
name—stooped over her, and took
hold of her hand, she opened her
eyes, and looked up at him. And
something she saw made her per-
fectly satisfied, and she smiled back
to him, and let her hand lay just
where it was. To this day I don't

know what it was he said to her, whether it was something out of his own head, or out of Scripture, or out of the Prayer Book itself, and, what's more, I don't care, and I didn't then. It was a blessed thing, and just what ma wanted, and a real peaceful look came over her thin old face.

And then he knelt down, and I knelt too, and he prayed. Seemed to me I'd never heard such a prayer, for it asked for just what I wanted for ma, just what she wanted herself, I know, but asked it a hundred times better than we could say it ourselves. " Did he read it out of a book ? " says Mrs. Lamson a week afterwards. And I didn't know ! When he finished and said Amen, ma said it too, very soft and weak. Then he leaned over her, and for a

second I was afraid he'd undo all
the good by saying something popish. So I smoothed ma's white hair
off of her forehead, and listened
close. And oh! what do you think
he was saying? He 'most whispered
it, but I heard. "Now I lay me
down to sleep," he says; and ma
says, so plain and clear, but softly,
"I pray the Lord my soul to keep."
And she turned her head a mite on
the pillow, shut up her eyes, and fell
asleep like a little child, never to
wake up in this world. Do you
think I didn't feel a mite different
after that about the Episcopals? But
I like my own church best.

And so I went on, learning lesson
after lesson. One thing I'd had
against the Baptists was their in-
sisting so on immersion. It seemed

so foolish. Sprinkling was our way,
and so I thought it must be the best
way, the only way. But one time,
of a Sunday noon, I happened to be
going by Blue River, and I saw a lot
of people on the bank. 'Twas a bap-
tism going on, and I stopped to see
it. You've seen them, and I won't
describe it. But I tell you one
thing, it brought home to me the
baptizings in the Bible as I'd never
had them brought before. I could
understand about going down into
the water and coming up out of the
water, and being baptized in Jordan.
I didn't stand very nigh, and I
couldn't see the folks to know them,
but I saw the robes and the river,
and heard the singing. I forgot
where I was, and 'most thought I
was seeing John or Paul, or—I'm a

bit afraid to say it, but you know
what I mean—mebbe our Lord Himself, baptizing or being baptized.
And I went away sorrowful, like the
young man in the Bible, for I'd been
thinking hard thoughts for years of
that very thing which seemed to me
now so beautiful and good and scrip-
tural. Then, after that, as I went
on associating with different Baptists, ministers and members, I saw
so many good things, true things,
amongst them, I can't tell you half.
I like my own church best, though.

Then there were the Presbyterians. I never saw any of them to
know them till I was more than
thirty years old. There wa'n't many
in New England, you know. But I
went visiting over to Hallsville,
where the factories are, and there

was a Presbyterian church there, and I went with Miss Starr, where I was staying. Dear me! it was just like our own church,—the long prayer, and the hymns, and the doxology, and the benediction. And the sermon couldn't have been bettered even among the Congos; it was sound right straight through, and full of scripture truth. Seems queer now that I should have been so surprised at this, but I was. To be sure, I'd heard that the difference betwixt them and the Congregationals was mostly in church government, but somehow I'd conceited that would show even in their meetings. I go to a Presbyterian church now; it's the nighest, you know, here in Factoryville. I love it, and the minister is one of the best men

that ever lived. But don't mistake
my meaning, somehow I like pa's
and ma's old church the best.

And so with the Methodists. I
was in the cars once, travelling down
to Vermont to see my cousin. There
was a gentleman sitting in front of
me, and I saw by his clothes or ways
or something that he was a minister.
Bimeby we fell into talk. I'll always recollect that talk, though I
couldn't tell you just how it went
along. But it always seems to me
that once in my life, like Paul, I
was caught up into the third heaven,
and, if I didn't see the Master Himself, I saw a man who'd talked with
Him, and walked with Him, and
knew Him as I'd never known Him.
And it was a Methodist preacher!
That's how I first came to think tol-

erant of them, but there's been a great deal since to keep it up. Still, I'm satisfied with our form of worship, and to me it's the best there is.

You see now how I was brought along, little by little, lesson after lesson, to see that there's something better and higher than sects and creeds, even though each man may like his own and his father's best. And I believe those lessons came from above as much as that great sheet did, let down by its four corners, to learn a similar lesson to Peter. So you see they've got a right to call me undenominational.

There's another thing. You'll take notice I haven't said anything about the Catholics. Well, I could! But then you're a Protestant, and so am I, and we're talking, just

now, about Protestant churches, and
haven't gone over all of them, either.
And then I don't want to scare you
more'n I can help.   But I'll just say
one single thing, and that's this :
the very best and heavenliest man I
ever saw, to my notion, the one that
seemed to me wouldn't have looked
out of place in heaven, even if you
hadn't altered him a mite in soul, or
even body,—his face was so shining
with love to God and man,—well, that
man was a Catholic, and a bishop.

But that's neither here nor there.
We're talking to-day about Protes-
tants.   I'm glad I'm one, and just as
glad that I'm a good, strong High
Church Congregational.   But I do
hope I've passed from death unto
life because, anyway, I love the
brethren.

AUNT
ABBY'S
HEAVEN

III AUNT ABBY'S HEAVEN

OF course, I know well enough, that folks in this world haven't got any right idee what heaven really is; it ain't in the natur' of things they can have. Scriptur' says right out plain that it hasn't entered into the heart of man to conceive what's up there. But seeing as you and me have talked over a good many things together, I'm going to tell you what I don't generally talk to folks about. I found out a long time ago that, however it might be with other people, as for me myself, I'd got so much of this world about me—the dust of the earth, as you might say, that I was made out of,—that I'd got, for a spell, to think about heaven and its doings in a kind of this-world way. I was so earthly myself that was the only way I could make it seem real and satisfying, and what I wanted for myself and my folks. So I took to sort of making-believe, " playing," as the children say, that this or that plain, homey, folksy thing was what they did up there. I knew all the time that it was making-believe, and that it wasn't a mite like the real heaven being prepared for them that love Him, and better than anything we can make up or guess about. But to me, just a poor, simple, country woman, my way seemed a help, and was a dreadful comfort anyway. I

didn't hold up these views of mine
to other folks as a general thing. I
was afraid of doing harm rather than
good, for it's a ticklish matter to
meddle with people's religious idees.
But a few times, when the folks
was just simple souls like me myself,
and I see they needed a little help in
some hard fight or dreadful sorrow,
why, I've given them a kind of hint
at what might be going on there—I
was careful never to say it really was
—and seems's if somehow it most
always helped 'em, for the time anyway.

Seems to me the first time I begun to do this way was when my
brothers, Elam and Horace, was
drowned. Pa and ma'd died before
that, about a year apart, and these
boys was almost everything I had to

love in the whole world. They went
off one morning, laughing and whist-
ling, full of their fun, and they was
fetched back at sundown cold and
stiff and still and dead. My heart
'most broke. I couldn't get a mite
of comfort all I could do. I was a
professor, and I tried to be resigned
and to think of the boys in heaven
and happy. They was good boys,
members of the church, and I felt
certain sure they was safe. And the
minister, Elder Leet, kept telling me
that I must think of them dwelling
in glory and chanting the praises of
Jehovah. I couldn't, I tell you, I
couldn't just then. They was great,
rugged, red-cheeked young fellers,
full of mischief and play, though not
a bit of harm in 'em, and just at first
I didn't even *want* to pictur' 'em all

changed and solemn, and so dreadful good. Oh! you understand,—don't you? I was sick with sorrow and all broke down, so that I couldn't just at once think the right thing, and trust my boys to Him that knew what was the very best for 'em.

I was sitting by the window the afternoon they was buried. The funeral was over, and the folks had gone away, and I was all alone in that still, dreadful, empty house. I looked out at the sky, all pinky and gilt-like after the sun going down, and I thinks to myself, "Oh! what are my boys doing now? If I only knew just what sort of a place they're in, I could bear it better." I was all wore out with crying and sorrowing, and mebbe I dozed a mite. Anyway, all of a sudden, I seemed to see heaven. 'Twas just like a real home down here, only big and light and shining. There was a window— likely's not many windows, but I only took notice of one, for my old father was sitting at it and looking out. And just behind him my mother was sitting. And while I was looking at 'em, I see pa start a little, and lean out as if he thought he see something, and then his face all brightened up and his eyes looked shining, and he turns 'round and cries out, his voice a-shaking a little, " Ma," he calls, " who do you think's a-coming up the street? Why, the boys, the boys, both on 'em, Elam and Horace ! I see 'em, I see 'em, there they be ; they'll be here in a minute." To my dying day I'll

never forget how those old faces
looked just for the little minute I
was let to see 'em. For 'twas over
dreadful quick. But it left something that's never got over yet, and
has helped me more'n I can tell you.
I knew in my own mind 'twas only
a kind o' dream, but I knew 'twould
come true in one sense, and there'd
be something up there just as good
and homey, and more so too. So I
went on dreaming that way whenever I needed it.

When I lost my little boy, the
only child I ever had, little Danny,
it most killed me. I won't trouble
you, though, with that, except one
part. The thing that worried me
and most broke my heart was to
think that I never should have him
again as he was when I see him last,

—a little yellow-haired feller going
on two. The minister and everybody told me he would be watching
for me up there, and that he would
be the one to learn me all the
wonderful things they'd learnt him
there; told me that "he knew
a'ready," as Elder Leet said, "a
thousand times more than I could
ever know here below." They
thought that would comfort me,
but it didn't. I thought I should
die, I wanted him to be a baby so, to
hold me tight, and be afraid without me. And yet somehow I wanted
him to grow up too, and not be a
stunted little thing, forever'n ever a
little baby boy going on two. I see
I must make believe again, and I
always think some one helped me.
For I saw myself dying and going up

there, and the very first one to come
and meet me was Danny. He wasn't
growed up at all, but the same little
curly-headed feller I'd buried, just
going on two. He stumbled along
with the very little steps I'd learnt
him myself and loved so, and he
stammered out the very same cunning little words I'd worked so to
learn him. And while I was holding him tight and babying him as I
used to, he seemed to grow bigger
and older, and he went on, I don't
know how fast or how slow, but I
see him go on and on till a big boy
and a bigger, a lad, and a youth, and
—a man. Just as any mother here
might see her boy grow up, only
without any worry or sorrow, scold-
ing or punishing or mourning over.
'Twas a dreadful comfort, the ma-

king-believe about that, and I've never stopped playing it was true.

Old Uncle Ezry Bouton was a real good old man, you know, but kind o' queer. Folks laughed at him, and hardly anybody understood him or made allowances. He thought he was a poet, and he wa'n't. But, dear me! that ain't uncommon. He used to make up verses, and go 'round reading 'em to folks till they was tired to death. And once he wrote a hymn, and set it to a tune he composed himself. 'Twa'n't a very original tune; 'twas a little like "Dennis," and a mite like "Naomi," and made you think of "Martyn," in some parts. And the words wasn't so great. But he was real proud of it. He was a Christian, if I ever see one, and I

really believe most of his pride
was on account of his thinking
he had got a real part of his own
in praising the Lord. But folks
laughed at it. I know part of it
run this way:

> " And all the angels flock around
> To hear the joyful, pious sound,"

and the tune he called " Wethersfield," after his native town. He
tried to get the choir to sing it, but
they wouldn't. He went to Miss
West, that give music lessons, and
asked her to try it over for him, but
she put him off. One day he died,
and he hadn't ever heard his own
hymn sung. I was thinking about
that when I heard he'd gone, and all
of a sudden I see one of my made-up
pictures. Uncle Ezry was coming

into his heavenly home. The light and the whiteness, and, more'n all, the music, sort of blinded him, and took his breath away. He'd never dreamt of anything like it, and he stopped and trembled, and was terrible scaret. All of a sudden the music hushed down a minute, and there seemed to be a kind of sign give to the angels—I never dast to think who give it—and they struck up singing real soft and nice,

> "And all the angels flock around
> To hear the joyful, pious sound."

'Twas Uncle Ezry's own hymn, and they were singing it to "Wethersfield." Seems's if I couldn't have made up out of my own head the look I seemed to see on Uncle Ezry's face then,—so dreadful surprised, sort of bashful and ashamed, but oh, so terrible, terrible happy!

When the greatest sorrow of all my life came to me, and I buried my husband, there was one thing kept coming up to me. 'Twas that verse in scripture about there not being any marrying or giving in marriage up there. To think of Thomas's not being my husband up there, and that I couldn't be to him more than anybody else, why, I couldn't bear it! Then one of my made-up pictures come right up before me, and I could see myself coming into that home up there, and Thomas a-meeting me. And as we stood together a spell afterwards, waiting, and me thinking whether we were going to be parted and sent to different mansions, some one come by—again I didn't dast to think who 'twas—and I heard a voice say, " Why, here's Thomas and Abby together again. Well, let them stay close by each other, they'll be happier that way." And I was satisfied.

I'm only telling you two or three of my make-believes. There've been hundreds more. Of course, they don't take the place o' the greatest hopes, the things we lot on most in looking ahead to that place,—I mean our Father's being there, and our Master always with them He's saved. But sometimes they help me to realize even those greatest things, for, as I said before, I'm an unlearnt, simple, country woman, and you can see for yourself I'm dreadful earthy.

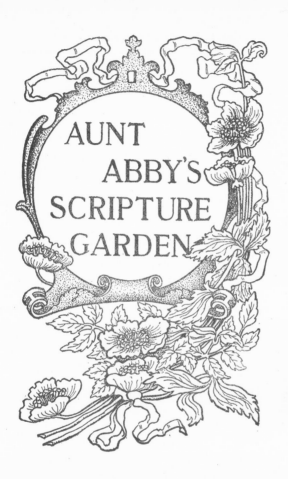

AUNT
ABBY'S
SCRIPTURE
GARDEN

IV   AUNT ABBY'S SCRIPTURE-GARDEN

YOU see it was this way. When I lived in Bartly I was dreadfully worked up about the children next door.

Some folks don't appear to worry about such things so long as they don't have any particular responsibility. But somehow I do feel responsible in a sort of way, and whenever I say those words "children next door," or "folks next door," seems as if I was owning that it was the next or nighest duty to take up, the having an eye to them and their best good. If those young ones next to me in Bartly had had a mother it would have been different. But they hadn't, and their pa didn't trouble himself much about them, and they were left to grow up by themselves without much of what I called the right sort of learning. They didn't go to any church, they nor their pa. He wasn't a bad man ; he was sober and hard working, but not religious. There were four children, two boys and two girls, running from six, up to thirteen year old, Janey, Martha, Nathan and Seth. They were real nice children, pleasant to each other, polite to folks, willing and busy and smart. But I could see they wa'n't getting the good they ought to get out of their lives, nor the happiness neither. For one thing they didn't know anything about the Bible, hadn't ever

read it or heard it read, nor had the
good old stories told to them most of
us recollect best, told in kind of easy
but solemn words in our mother's, or
mebbe our father's, voice, when we
were mites of young ones. That
seemed a dreadful pity. I'd part
with anything sooner than that remembering, now that those voices of
pa's and ma's have been still such a
long, long spell.

I got to knowing the children
pretty quick. I'm fond of young
ones and they're good for me. I
didn't want to scare them just at first
by preaching, or anything that appeared like it. But after a spell,
when we'd got to be real friends and
playfellows like, I begun to think
what I could do. In the first place,
I saw right off that I must put their

going to Sabbath-school out of the question. Their father wouldn't have it. He wasn't exactly an unbeliever, but he'd had some things happen that gave him a feeling against churches, both ministers and members. I hoped that would wear off some day, but meantime what was I going to do with those children? I tried reading the Bible to them, telling them about it, and trying to make them read it, but somehow for the life of me I couldn't interest them. They liked other kinds of stories and games, but they seemed to have some of their father's feeling about the scripture; 't any rate, it didn't interest them a mite.

Well, thinking it over one day, I said to myself, "What *does* interest

them, then?" And the answer came
in a jiffy, "Why, posies."

That was nothing but the truth.
For some reason or other every one
of those young ones set everything
by posies. Seems their ma'd been
that way, too. Mebbe they'd copied
it from her, seein' how much she
liked such things, or perhaps it was
born in them, and they took after
her by nature. Any way they liked
all growing things, plants and trees,
posies and herbs. They'd always
take notice of them, bring them in
from the woods, plant them in their
yards or in boxes or tin cans in the
house, talk about them and ask their
names. But how was this liking of
theirs going to help me learn them
the good there was in the Bible?
Just telling them that God made the

plants and trees and took care of
them, and that they could read all
about Him and His ways in scripture, why, that's sound doctrine, but
somehow I felt it wouldn't work
with that family just at first.   I
must begin careful, or they'd think
I was preaching.

It took me quite a time to think
it out, and when I began I didn't
really know exactly how it would
work and how far I could carry it.
I don't recollect now exactly how I
put it to the children first-off, but I
proposed somehow at last that we
should start a scripture-garden.   The
name struck them.   Children like
queer, uncommon names, and they
wanted to know right off what that
was.   I told them that there was
lots in the Bible about plants and

such things, and it would be real
nice to see how many of the posies
that book told about we could find
and set out. They were interested
right away. Young ones all like to
collect, if it's buttons or stamps or
horse-chestnuts, and they were in a
hurry to begin. We marked off a
corner of the yard, and the children
put up a sign, a stick with a board on
it and the name—Janey printed it—
Scripture-Garden.

They didn't have any Bibles of
their own, and I told them they
could come over and use my big-
print one, at first, anyway. I had
thought up a few plants to start with
till they should get interested enough
to hunt for themselves.

We begun with lilies, for I told
the children it seemed as if there

was more about those flowers than
any other kind. I read to them
about building the temple, and the
lily-work put onto the pillars and
the porch and round the edge of the
molten sea. And I let them look up,
helpin' them a little, of course,
verses like " Israel shall grow as the
lily," and " feeding among the lilies."
Then I begun to repeat " as the lily
among thorns," and Martha struck
right in with, " That's another plant ;
we must have some thorns." I
praised her a mite for thinking of
that, but I said we must keep to
lilies now. And then I told them
about that beautiful verse, " Consider
the lilies, how they grow." And
when I'd spoken of that, why, it
came in natural you see, to tell them
a little about who said it. Not too

much, just at first, for fear they'd
think I was preaching, but it was a
beginning, you see. Then we talked
about what kind of lilies we'd have.
I had a root of yellow day-lilies at
the corner of the house, and I let
them dig it up and set it out in their
own garden. Miss Susan Bowles let
us have some white ones, and I told
them that the next time I went over
to the north district I'd buy some
tiger-lilies from some of the folks
there that had plenty. I said that,
though I didn't really know whether
they had just that specie of lily in
Bible times, it always seemed to me
they were something the sort our
Lord was thinking of when He said
that King " Solomon in all his glory
was not arrayed like one of these."
They're so kind of gay and showy

and striking with their bright red flowers all spotty with brown. Then Seth surprised me by speaking up and saying, "Why, Aunt Abby, it says ' the lilies *of the field*,' and tiger-lilies grow in gardens. But I know a kind that's wild and grows all themselves in the fields and the meadows, and they're gayer and strikin'er than tiger ones, I think."

To be sure! I hadn't thought of those wild ones, and I told the children they could go down the next day, and dig up, careful, some of the roots, and put them in the lily part of their garden, so they'd bloom that very summer, for 'twas May when we started the scripture-garden. Then I told them about a pretty hymn we used to sing at Sabbath school to a real nice tune :

"By cool Siloam's shady rill
  How fair the lily grows!
How sweet the breath, beneath the hill,
  Of Sharon's dewy rose!"

And all together cried out, "Rose! There's another flower. Is it in the Bible, Aunt Abby?" I remembered "I am the rose of Sharon," and after a spell I thought of a verse about the desert "blossoming like the rose." It was easy enough to fix the rose part of the garden, for there was a clump of cinnamon roses right there at one end of the patch of ground I'd given them.

By this time the children had got so interested they couldn't wait for me to look up plants in the Bible, but they'd spend hours, snuggling close together over the big book on the table, their heads almost touching, they crowded so close. **And** they found so many things! I can't recollect them all myself just now. They had mint, I know, with its soft, fuzzy leaves and purply blooms, sweet smelling and spicy. They got leave to widen their garden a mite so's to take in my old apple-tree. They said they found lots about apples in the Bible and they must have one. They found briers talked about, too, so they brought home a sweetbrier with its pretty pink flowers, from over by the pond.

By and by, as the scripture plants almost ran out, and it was harder work finding verses about them, there was a great time looking for more Bibles, so they could each have one to use. Then I sent and bought four nice ones, and gave each child one of his own. How tickled they

were! They took them home, and
I suppose they were always a hunt-
ing, and searching, and talking
about the plants and their garden,
for one day they came trooping in at
my gate, so excited and pleased,
bringing a little bush, roots and all.
It had little bits of pink double
flowers like teenty roses all over it,
and I saw it was a flowering-almond.
" Pa give it to us," they called out,
all at once. " He found about it in
the Bible last night after we'd gone
to bed, where it says ' the almond-
tree shall flourish.' So he went up
to General Billings's before breakfast
to ask for this one, and fetched it
home to surprise us."

Now I don't believe myself that's
the kind of almond the Bible means.
I guess that sort has the nuts we eat

with raisins after the pies on Thanks-
giving days. But you may be sure
I didn't say so, nor discourage that
man in his first experiment with
scripture-gardening. So they set out
their pretty little bush, and that
day they found a lot more verses
about almond-trees and almonds.
They had a grape-vine running over
the fence between their corner and
the road, and they could say off ever
so many passages about vines and
grapes, and the blood of grapes.
They had a little border of soft green
grass all around their garden. "For
you know, Aunt Abby," said Nathan,
"there's most as much about grass
in the Bible as there is about grapes
and lilies." One day Martha came
in, her hands scratched and bleeding,
holding a big field thistle with its

pricky leaves and stem, and purple
flowers. She said she had found
three verses about thistles. She was
a mite hurt and disappointed when
I told her she better not plant one,
for it would send its seed all over
the place and bring up lots of pricky,
hurting weeds to trouble the neighbors as well as ourselves. But Seth
—dear little Sethy, even then, before
he went away from us, I thought
him the best, the thoughtfulest of
them all—Seth chirked her up by
giving her a slip of myrtle with its
dark green leaves and blue flowers.
I had given it to him from my
myrtle bed, where it ran all about
and grew so thick. And we had
read the verses about " I will plant
in the wilderness the myrtle," and
" Instead of the thorn shall come up

the myrtle-tree." He set everything
by that vine, but he gave it up,
cheerful, to Martha, and she was
dreadful pleased.

Well, before that summer was over
I had done what I'd hoped to do,
and a good deal more. Those children had all got some idea of what
the Bible was and how much there
was in it. When they were looking
up the plants they'd come upon
other things, and stop to read about
them, and I'd often hear them talking among themselves about the
Bible stories and about those best
things I wanted them to think of
and know. Their pa he took an interest, too, seeing them so full of it,
and he studied up nights sometimes
to give them a surprise, and was so
set up when he could find something

they hadn't noticed. 'Course I don't
mean to say that it made a full
grown christian all at once out of
him or the children either, but it
gave them the first start in the right
way, and that's a big thing. As I
said before, Sethy was the best, the
thoughtfulest of all the four. He
was the most interested in the
scripture-garden, so in earnest in
finding out the plants and learning
all about them. But it worried him
dreadfully, there being so many
talked about in the Bible that he
couldn't get for his garden and nobody else could. He was set on
having a pomegranate-tree, and he
wanted aloes and cassia and olives
and figs, trees and plants that can't
be got in this part of the world anywheres. Once he ran in and asked

me, in his queer little old-fashioned
way, if I thought he could get an
almug-tree over at Sheldon—that
was the biggest town near us. I
didn't even know there was such a
thing, and I thought mebbe he was
trying to say almond. But he said
it over again and spelt the name,
and told me they were real common
in Ophir, for the Bible said the ships
brought in a " great plenty " of them
from there. But most of all Sethy
wanted palms. He liked the story
of the people throwing palm
branches down before Jesus when
He was coming to Jerusalem, and he
was always wishing he'd been there
to throw just one. And he knew
about Deborah's palm and the place
that was called the city of palm-
trees, and—oh, how much that boy

could tell you about palms and what
was said about them in the good
book. " I'd like to go to Elim,
wouldn't you, Aunt Abby ? " he said
one time. " What for ? " I says.
" Why,—don't you remember ?—
there were seventy palm-trees there.
Just think of it, seventy whole ones,
and I've never seen one."

Somehow, of all the four children,
he was the one that seemed to learn
the real inside meaning of what he
found in the Bible and to take it
right into his little heart. And he
was the one to leave us. Before
the scripture-garden was dry and
shrivelled, the lilies of the field, the
rose of Sharon, the almond-tree that
flourished, the grass that God had so
clothed with green and softness, before all these had gone to sleep for

the winter, little Seth had left us all.
Just a few days of fever and aching,
a few sort of wandering words, most
of them about his garden and the
lilies and Him that loved and talked
about them; then just at the last a
little low, stammering whisper we
couldn't quite catch except that
'twas about palms and throwing
them down before Somebody, and
the little boy was at rest.

And I was dreadful glad to think
he'd had that scripture-garden with
all it learnt him. I knew he'd never
miss it where he'd gone. To the
rest of us that little posy patch meant
more than ever now, as it faded away
with the fall and winter and grew dry
and brown and dead looking. The
children wondered if it would wake
up in the spring. I knew it would.

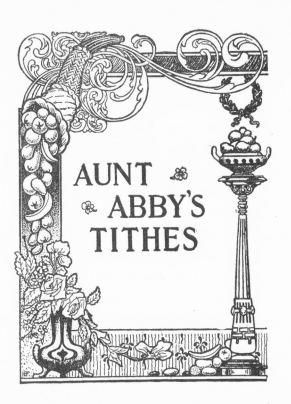

AUNT ❧ ❧ ABBY'S TITHES

V   AUNT ABBY'S TITHES

AFTER I joined the church, and so put myself down regular on the Lord's side, I began to consider just what I ought to do about my charities. I was born and raised sort of free-handed,—took it from both pa and ma. So I didn't try to see how little I could give away and keep up appearances and satisfy my conscience, but how much I could spare and yet get along. I never had a head for figures. I was always at the foot of the arithmetic class in school,—don't really know the multiplication-table to this day, and am forever getting mixed up and

muddled over the bills at the store
or on the farm.

I knew I must be dreadful particular in this matter, and, if I'd got
to make mistakes I must make them
on the right side; I mean I must
manage to give too much rather than
too little. One of pa's old sayings
was, "It's better to slop than to
skimp," and that's truer in giving to
the Lord than in anything else. I
didn't like to ask anybody about it.
I knew better than other folks about
what I owned, and, particular, how
much I'd had from the Lord to be
grateful for and pay back. But still
I really didn't know myself just
what my income was, nor how much
I could afford to part with. I
owned the place where I lived,—a
little house with a few acres of land.

I had a little money in the savings
bank, and there were a few other
things that brought me in something every year; but just how
much it all came to I didn't know.
And again, what part, how much of
it all, I ought to give back in charity, I wasn't exactly sure. But I
thought it over, and studied up the
Bible, and, of course, prayed over it
some, and by and by it seemed to
come to me. I found out from the
Bible that the least anybody ought
to give was a tenth of what he had.
It's called a tithe in some places, but
Deacon Blodgett said that was the
same thing, and meant a tenth part.
But, as I said before, I didn't know
how much property I had, so how
could I divide it by ten, and get a
tithe of it?

Well, I soon saw that the only
way I could fix it and be certain
sure I wasn't skimping the Lord's
share was this : I must divide every
single thing as it came along by ten,
and when I'd got the answer to the
sum, I must give that away right off,
before I forgot about it, always adding a little to it, for fear I hadn't
divided right, knowing my bad head
for figures. You have no idea how
well that way worked, and works
still, for I always do it to this day.
I'll show you.

There were my hens, for one thing.
I had quite a lot, and they were
good layers most times. Well, say I
got fifteen eggs one day. As soon as
I'd counted them I'd divide them by
ten. It would go once and something over, so, of course, I'd call it

twice. There'd be two eggs that didn't belong to me, but to the Lord or His people. Then there was the allowing, as I call it,—the adding on for fear I hadn't divided right; and that made three. Of course, I picked out the biggest, if there was any difference, and in some ways or other those three eggs went where they belonged. Sometimes they were sold, and the money paid into the treasury; sometimes they went just as eggs to some of the Lord's sick or poor, or to somebody doing His work.

Then my garden: the vegetables, and the fruit, and the flowers,—they were all divided the same way, as fast as they came on. 'Twas hard work for me, with my poor head for figures, to find out just how much a tenth part of a bushel was, when I had my roots dug,—the potatoes and turnips, carrots, and so on. I couldn't do it on paper or the slate. I just had to take each bushel itself, and lay them out in ten parts, by looks or counting. Then I'd allow, of course, feeling pretty sure I'd made some mistake, and generally add a little from nine of the heaps to the Lord's pile,—and there it was, you see, all done. 'Twas a good deal of work, but real interesting. Pumpkins were easy. They were big, and counted quick. Beans and peas were pretty difficult, but cabbages plain and easy.

My posies didn't bring in any money; there wasn't any sale for such things in the village, of course, so they must be given away just as

they were. But there were always
sick people to send a little bunch to,
or poor folks that hadn't any gardens, and many, many times there
were the dead, with them they'd left
sorrowing, wanting to lay something
white and sweet and comforting on
their breasts or in their cold, still
hands. And there was the meeting-
house to look out for Sundays with
the pitcher of Canterbury bells or
fox-gloves or poppies or pinks.
Congregationals—I was always one
of them, you know—didn't put
flowers in the meeting-house much
those days. But it seemed a good
thing to me, our Master having
made so much of posies, and they
themselves having so many little
kind of sermons in them. So I begun doing it, and somehow nobody

stopped me, though there was some talk at first, and the story got around that Abby Coles—that's me, you know—was going over to the Episcopals. Then there was my herb corner, where I raised thyme and sweet-marjoram and mint and summer-savory. I just admired to do the dividing up of that, for it made me think of the "tithes of mint, anise, and cummin" the Bible tells of. You wouldn't think there was much use for such herbs in the Lord's work, but there was. There was stuffing for the tenth part of my chickens—I didn't keep turkeys—to have sage or sweet-marjoram or summer-savory or all three in, as folks chose; and there were the sausages, tithes of them to be seasoned up for the minister and his big family,—

he had quivers full of children,—
and for old Captain Lee, Aunt Lois
Worthy, 'Lias Bates, and all the
rest of our poor folks. And there
was hardhack and boneset and
motherwort, and lots of other cur-
ing, healing things for the sick and
ailing. Dear me! my tenth part of
that herb-bed had to have lots of *allowing* to make it go 'round.

Well, so I did with everything,
you see. The interest I got from
the savings-bank I tithed each time
it came in, always allowing more on
that than on other things, because
of my poor head for figures, and my
being afraid I should do the sum
wrong. And so with the rent for my
pasture that John Walker hired for
his cattle. He didn't pay very regular, sometimes not at all. But, of

course, that didn't make any difference; I'd got to take a tenth of the
price he'd ought to 'a' paid, besides
the allowing.

Of course, I've only told you a
part of the story. 'Twould take me
a year to tell about everything,—
how I measured the milk from my
cow when it was new, and then the
cream when it was skimmed; how,
when my pigs were killed, I tithed
the meat,—spareribs, hams, pork,
and all, each by itself. My calves
too,—the veal, the liver, and the
head. I gave a tenth part of the use
of my horse—old Jack—to the sick
or poor, the minister or funerals. I
tithed my hay, my oats, my buck-
wheat, and always every single time,
of course, I allowed, to make sure I
was right and honest.

This rule of mine worked sort of queer sometimes, and turned out almost comical. I recollect once I'd been busy house-cleaning, and somehow I'd forgotten how near out the victuals in the house was. I went to set the table for tea, and I found there wasn't hardly anything in the closet but one huckleberry pie and three doughnuts. I'd got into such a habit of tithing I begun to divide those provisions right off, though I really had done it before on baking-day, and sent out my tenth and the allowing. I undertook to cut that pie into ten pieces, but you know how difficult huckleberry pie is. The juice would run so and the berries squeeze out till I couldn't tell one piece from another, and, come to the tenth, there didn't hardly seem to be anything to it, even with the allowing. So I see I might as well take the whole pie, and call it a tithe, and I ran over to poor Miss Randy Shaw's with it. When I came back, I had another hard sum to do, for there were my three doughnuts to divide by ten! I was too tired to try to do that, so I eat one with my cup of tea, and laid away the others for little lame Billy, down the west road.

There were lots of other things I can scursely put into words,—sums you can't do by any rule of arithmetic, and yet must be taken into account and tithed. There were the kind things folks did for me, such a heap of them; for everybody's always so good to me, and I'm sure I don't know why. Those things must be divided somehow, and at least a tenth part of them passed on to them that needs them. There was my Bible and all it holds; that must have its tithe sent to those that haven't got it,—the heathen here at home and way off in distant lands. And my church,—I'm Congregational, you know,—some ways I must give part of what I got out of that. There was my minister, Mr. Jessup, too. It made me smile for a minute when I first thought of dividing him by ten. He was dreadful poor, as far as flesh goes, and seemed as though a tithe of him wouldn't go very far. But, dear me! the goodness and kind deeds and faithful work for his people made enough of him to divide by a hundred.

And then—I mean to speak very solemn and with great respect and reverence about this—there was the greatest gift I'd had in all my poor, selfish life, the Christmas present, as I like to call it in my heart. I tried real hard to give my whole share and more of what I owed Him for that, and help folks that hadn't my privileges to get its peace and comfort. I don't think there was any need of stopping at a tenth part in that matter.

Well, I've made a long story out of my tithing,—haven't I? But you asked me about it, you know. And it does seem to me such a good way to lay out your charities, and such an easy one, too. For, as far as I can see, it comes out just about right, —that is, if you divide every single

thing as it comes along by ten, and
don't wait or forget.   But remember,
you must always *allow*, even if you
think you have a head for figures.
Seems to me each year, as I look
back and count up, that my allow-
ance is about as big as my tithes,
though I don't see how that can be.
But I never was much at arithmetic,
—that's the thing of it.

AUNT ABBY
ON
FRIENDSHIP

VI AUNT ABBY ON FRIENDSHIP

WHEN I was a girl I used to think and talk a great deal about friendship. Most young folks do, I guess. It's a kind of nice-sounding, sentimental word, and lots has been said and writ about it. There was a book that always laid on ma's best room table—it had a red cover and matched the carpet and curtains—called "Friendship's Offering," and there were real pretty verses in it. And there was a piece we used to sing to a tune named Friendship, a sort of jumpy, up and down tune. The words began,

"Friendship to every willing mind
Offers a heavenly treasure."

And there were ever so many stories
in different books about friends and
all they did for each other. I used
to think about the subject a good
deal and wish I had one of the kind
of friends that would die for me, and
things like that. And I'd sit by the
hour and think how fine 'twould be
to have somebody set so much by me
that she'd follow me to the ends of
the earth and give up everything for
me, and mebbe mourn herself to
death on my grave if I was taken
away first. Or I'd get thinking how
she'd save me from drowning or being burnt up or run over, and how
she'd lose her own life by drowning
or burning or being run over, and be
glad to do it for me, her beloved
friend. I'd really cry hard about it
as I'd go all over it in my mind,

it seemed so real and so dreadful mournful and nice.

Well, I kept choosing friends, one at a time, and each time I'd think it was going to be one of the friendships you read about. But somehow it didn't turn out that way. Mebbe she—the friend—would give up to me and do things for me, first-off, but it wouldn't last. She'd get tired giving up and expect me to do some of the sacrificing, and then I'd be disappointed and discouraged, and feel as if I was a kind of martyr. And I'd write compositions about this world's being a fleeting show, and how nobody appreciated folks whose hearts was crying out for a friend, and all that silly stuff young folks talk and write.

There was Jane Langworthy. I

took her for my intimate friend one time. We went to school together, and we sat at the same desk and kept together in our lessons and were always whispering secrets and going about with our arms 'round each other. I asked her if she was willing to die for me, and she said she was, and I believed her and was real satisfied. But one time when I was head of the spelling class and set on keeping my place, Jane spelt a word I missed and went above me, and my faith in true friendship was shook for a long spell.

Then I had Mercy Evans. That lasted longer than most any of my everlasting friendships, for Mercy was a dreadful pleasant girl and real unselfish. But once we were talking together on the way to singing-school, and I asked her if she would be willing to be burnt at the stake sooner than deny her friendship for me. Well, I didn't suppose she'd even stop to think, but she did. She sort of colored up and looked troubled, and I says, " Why, of course, you'd go to the stake, cheerful, if you had to choose betwixt that and denying me, wouldn't you?" And Mercy says, very low and stammering, " Oh, I hope I might, but I'm so afraid I wouldn't. I ain't a bit good about standing pain, you know, and I *might* give in." I was that disappointed I could hardly speak, but as soon as I found my voice, I just up and told her what I thought of her and what a failure she was as a real, true, self-denying friend.

So it went on, but I can't remember all of my different friendships nor what broke each one up. But I do remember plain just how I came to see things different and to know what friendship really means. My friend that time was Maria Anderson. She was real pretty to look at, with heaps of shining yellow hair, pink cheeks, and big blue eyes. I guess it was her good looks made me first think of taking her for my intimate friend. She wasn't much at studying and was 'most always near the foot of the class, and she wasn't very well off, her folks being about the poorest in the village. But she talked beautiful about friendship and promised to stand by me till death and give up everything for me, even her life, if it was necessary. I thought this time I'd found just what I'd been looking for so long. But after a spell I began to see faults in Maria. Spite of all her talk about giving up, I could see she managed to get her own way, or tried to, at any rate. She expected my help in her lessons and writing compositions; she hinted at wanting my prettiest hair ribbons and bows. She got me to introduce my boy friends to her and then sort of took them away from me, she being so much nicer to look at. Fact is, she didn't seem to do anything for me in friendship's name except to talk and promise.

'Twas just at that time when I was seeing all this and was disappointed and discouraged, for about the twentieth time in my life, that

something happened. 'Twasn't anything out of the common; at least
it didn't appear to be at first. I was
turning over the leaves of my Bible,
looking for a good verse to say at
weekly prayer-meeting, when my
eye fell on the word " friend," and I
stopped to read what it said. It was
that beautiful verse, " Greater love
hath no man than this, that a man
lay down his life for his friend."
Well, in my narrow, selfish way of
looking at the subject, poor, silly
girl that I was, I says to myself,
" Oh, how true that is! But where
shall I ever find such a friend, one
that would really and truly lay down
her life for me?"

All of a sudden,—for the very
first time in my life, if you'll believe it,—came into my mind the

question, " What about *your* doing
that for a friend?" I felt kind of
ashamed, even though I was all
alone by myself, but I tried to get
around it by saying, " We're not
talking about that side of it; that's
another question." But I knew all
the time it wasn't another question,
but the same, only more important.
I tried to get it out of my head, so I
thought I'd look up some other
verses about friends and friendship,
thinking they might give different
views. I had a little leather-cov-
ered book, Brown's Concordance,
and I began to look it over. I
found a good many verses abouf
friends, such as " A friend loveth at
all times,"—not only when things
go right, you see,—and " Thine own
friend, and thy father's friend, for-

sake not "—not even if they're not quite perfect and seem a mite selfish. And then, turning over the pages, I kept coming upon passages about our dealings with our " brothers," which must be about the same as friends, the forgiving them, and bearing with them, and giving up for them, and doing for them, and " by love, serving one another," bearing each other's burdens, being long suffering. And I struck by chance (mebbe it wasn't chance) on those verses about charity ; its never failing, its suffering long, its bearing all things, believing all things, hoping all things, enduring all things. Dear me, by that time I almost crawled under the table, I was so ashamed of what I had called my friendships.

But all that was nothing when I came, sudden like, upon this verse, "Henceforth I call you not servants, but friends." It was the Lord, our Master, who said that, you know. And He said it to them that were weak and foolish and full of mistakes, if nothing worse. He said it to Peter who was going to deny Him in the very first trouble that came; to Thomas, so full of doubtings and unbelief, to all of them that, when trials came, "forsook Him and fled." He called them friends, with all their sins and selfish ways, and was going to lay down His life for them, —and He did it. I knew all this before, but somehow I hadn't thought of it in this connection, when I was trying to find out what friendship was and why I hadn't ever got the right kind of friend.

That was one of the great waking-ups of my life, and I've had a good many. I don't mean to say I'm the right kind of friend now. I can see such self-seeking, mean, uncharitable things in my friendships always still, but I know now what they'd ought to be. Maria Anderson is about my most intimate friend still. We kept on, you see, after that time. I don't know as she's changed so dreadful much, but I look at things different. There's always two sides to a friendship, and she's got the side that lets me do for her, help her, make allowances for her. That seems to me the hardest side. I could scursely stand it to have that side, unless it was laid upon me so's

I could see I'd ought to take it.
And I've got the side of helping,
giving up, sacrificing,—in a very
small way that hardly deserves the
name,—seeing the happiness I can
give her and that she's willing to
take. Mine's the easiest side, you
see, but I didn't seek it out; it
seemed to come that way naturally.
And she does fit into her part real
well, and I love her for it. It almost seems sometimes that she goes
out of her way to give me chances
to do for and help her. There's
times when I am wishing for some
new way to show my friendship for
her, and all of a sudden she'll let me
know there's some one little thing
she wants and has set her mind on,
and that I could get for her. And I
do it, gladly enough, I tell you, and

she takes it so surprised and so thankful, and there comes a little more love for her in my heart and a beautiful new thing into our friendship.

Sometimes—not very often, not quite frequent enough to suit me— the thing I see she wants takes a real sacrificing and giving up on my part, and that's splendid and makes my heart too full to hold. It was that way about the little home of her own she's got now, down the street there. She let me see that she just longed to own that place, and I managed to surprise her with it one birthday. I found I couldn't quite do that without parting with my wood lot that I'd sort of held on to because pa left it to me. And the letting that wood lot go so't I could buy the little home for Maria was 'most the best thing that ever came into our friendship, for it hurt a little, and I was dreadful glad.

And there's lots of little bits of things she lets me do. She never liked preserving and pickling or making jell. She always lets me do them for her, and generally her cake and pies too. And her posy garden is prettier than mine now since I took to taking care of it for her. I don't waste my time now, pottering over my own plants in the selfish way I used to, and I'm so proud and pleased when folks talk about what a faculty for gardening Miss Anderson's got, and kind of hint that she beats me. And so as to the work she takes home from the sewing society. She has a queer trouble in her back that makes her nervy and sort of weak if she sews, while I really like to have a needle in my fingers, so it works just right, her part and mine. And, of course, there's no need of talking about our little ways outside, so I get a little pride again in knowing folks think my best friend is a good seamstress.

Oh, I get my full share out of this friendship, you better believe. I'm too selfish not to have that. It's better to be a friend than have a friend, I hold, but they come to the same thing after all. Don't call yourself a friend and be thinking the everlasting time what the other side of the friendship can do for you. But be a friend for the sake of what you can do for the other, what you can give or give up, what sorrow you can bear for him, what sacrifice you can make, what good to his body or, more than all, to his soul.

How I do run on! And I ought to be home this instant minute, steeping some wild valerian. Maria Anderson feels as if she was going to have a gone spell, and she always thinks my steeping is a lot better than any she can do, she's so partial to me, for I'm her most intimate friend, you know.

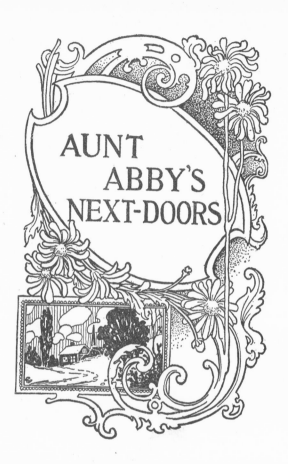

AUNT
ABBY'S
NEXT-DOORS

VII AUNT ABBY'S "NEXT-DOORS"

I WAS telling you once how I always felt about folks that lived next door, how it seemed to lay a kind of responsibility on me as a sort of next door or nighest duty. Well, that notion of mine brought a lot of queer things into my life; some of them pleasant, some funny, and some real mournful. I always called such neighbors "next-doors," and I remember so many of them.

There was Miss Silvy Blow that lived in the other half of my house in Factoryville. I didn't get to know her for quite a spell, though I tried hard. She kept to herself and never would look up or speak when we met on the steps or anywheres. And she had such a sort of cross, stand-off look on her face, a real unhappy expression too. I found she was deaf and dreadful touchy about it, and unhappy and suspecting and unresigned. I felt terrible sorry for her. Seemed as if I must do something to help her and brighten her up, and bimeby I got the chance and I've always been so glad and thankful. Dear me, how many things I've had to be thankful for, and more than anything else, the lots of chances to help folks that have been sent to me. There ain't many people so blest.

I don't remember exactly how we first got to speaking. But any way after a spell Miss Silvy appeared to see I was friendly and interested in her, and she wasn't so stand-off with me, and before many weeks we were good friends. One day she showed how much she liked and trusted me by letting out the whole mournful story of her deafness and how it was spoiling her whole life. It cut her off, she said, from everybody, and she was so lonesome and miserable. Folks avoided her, the children wouldn't come nigh her, and she was always thinking people were saying things about her when she saw them talking and couldn't hear them. Poor, poor thing, how I did pity her, though I saw plain enough she was making a dreadful mistake. I was 'most afraid to say a word for fear it would be the wrong thing, and so do more harm

than good, but I just couldn't let her
go on in that dreadful way without
at any rate trying to help. So first
I let her see plain that I was real
sorry for her and felt for her and felt
with her. That never does a mite
of harm whatever you do afterwards.
Even if you feel you've got to find a
little fault or give a bit of advice or
point out some small mistakes or
wrong-doings, be sure to show your
liking and your sympathizing first,
and they'll take the other dose a
heap easier and better; at least
that's the way it's been with me.
And after I'd done that—done it
right from my heart too, for I did
feel terrible sorry for her, so that
my eyes got sort of wet and teary
and she saw it—then I begun to
show her the other side. First place

I made her smile a little by quoting
one of my old grandma's rhyming
proverbs—she had one for every
occasion—

> " Be but a little deaf and blind,
>   If happiness you wish to find."

Then I told her there seemed to me
lots of truth in that. There's so
many, many things in this world
we'd all be better off for not hearing,
but it's hard to shut our ears to them.
But as for her, I says to Miss Silvy,
why her ears were shut for her. So
she wasn't always hearing the gossip,
the ill-natured, spiteful things folks
said. For they was generally, not
always, said without stopping to
think and so was hardly ever spoken
out loud and plain and deliberate as
they must be said to a person a mite
hard of hearing. I'm sure you've no-

ticed that, yourself, how folks scursely ever sit down and say out loud into a deaf person's ear the hateful unkind things about other people that they'd soon enough say, sort of under their breath, or in hintings and shakes of the heads and half said meanings. That was one thing, I told Miss Silvy, that had made me most wish I was a mite hard of hearing myself. And another was the being able to shut yourself up any time and think of those great subjects that always seem to need a still time and a shut-in place for thinking about. Other folks that hear every little disturbing noise have to enter into a closet and shut the door with their own hands. But with deaf people, there it is all done for them by Somebody else. And as for the suspecting part,

the being afraid folks are saying
something bad about you when you
see they're speaking and can't hear
them, why seems's if 'twould work
the other way. Why not get into
the habit of suspicioning they're saying something so good of you they're
afraid to let you hear? For lots of
times, that's the truth. And I told
Miss Silvy two or three kind, pleasant things I, myself, had heard folks
say about her, when I could see by
her face at the time she'd thought
they were talking against her.

And as for the children's not liking her and their keeping out of
the way, why, was it all their fault?
I didn't want to blame it on her,
but I just sort of hinted that she
hadn't given the boys and girls in
that district much reason to think she

wanted them around, and I was so glad I could tell her what little Sarah Ann Mills said the other day. She'd been over there on an errand and she said she see a rag baby up on the shelf and she did want so to take it, but she was afraid of Miss Silvy. Then the little thing went on, " I wish't I wasn't so 'fraid of her, for she looks's if she wasn't very comfor'ble and I'd like to amuse her." Miss Silvy's eyes got a mite damp and she says, " That was Mary's doll baby, my little sister that died. Sarah Ann looks a mite like Mary, now I think of it, and she can come and play with that doll any time she wants to ; you tell her so."

Dear me, I can't tell you all I said to her. You would have said it better and thought of more of those con-

soling things. But I recollect one
thing I dwelt on was that deafness
seemed to bring your friends so close
up to you. They had to look right in
your face and speak right into your
ear, so that everything they said
seemed meant just for you alone and
nobody else, kind of confidential, you
know. You see my talk was all
plain, common truth that everybody
knows and told in my poor way.
But Somebody blessed it and made it
take effect, and Silvy Blow got to be
a different kind of woman before
long. Her face lost that unhappy,
fretful look and got a real peaceful,
sweet expression, and folks went to
see her a great deal, particular when
they were in trouble and they told
their sorrows right into her ears and
she was never tired of hearing and

trying to help. And the children, my! the house was full of boys and girls from morning to night. Come to find out Miss Silvy was a great hand at making rag dolls and painting up their faces, and the young ones said her cookies and turnovers couldn't be beat and she knew more games and stories then anybody else in Factoryville.

The children's shrill, clear voices made her hear real easy. But there were two or three sort of bashful young ones that liked best to get close up to her and talk right into her ear, and she loved that. Sarah Ann Mills was one of them and it was pretty to see her snuggling up to Miss Silvy her little pink mouth close to her ear while she told her things. I heard her one time saying softly that way, " I'm real sorry, Miss Silvy, if it hurts you being deaf, but I can't help loving you best that way, it's so nice to tell things right into your inside where your heart is." " Bless you, deary," says Miss Blow, " you always looked like my little sister, Mary, and you favor her more every single day."

I've made a long story out of that one next door neighbor. I was going to tell you about a lot of them but I haven't time for much more to-day. There was poor Martha Merrit that thought she wasn't elected and so couldn't be saved and did nothing else from day's end to day's end but mourn and lament over her lost condition. I had such a time with her. For a long spell I argued with her and tried my best

to convince her that there was hope
for her and for all of us poor sinners
and to show her where that hope
lay. But it was wasted breath,
time thrown away. And bimeby I
got tired and I took another way.
I asked her if she was certain sure
she was going to be lost and she said
she was, for she hadn't been elected
and she knew she should be doomed
to everlasting woe. " Well, then," I
says, " if it's sure and certain why
there ain't any use in trying to do
anything about it. But there are
lots and lots of folks that there's
hope for still and they need somebody to learn them what's right and
to help them and comfort them.
So," I says, " as there's not a bit of
use doing anything for your own
soul why you're just the very one to

work for others, having plenty of time, you see. And I'll tell you some things you can do right off." Well, I don't know why, but it seemed to strike her as something new and right too. She was a kind-hearted woman and a sensible one, get her off that one idea that she was almost crazy over. She took up the work I picked out for her and she did it, did it well and kindly, and I gave her more. She got terrible interested in it, and a little at a time she forgot herself and her not being elected and—oh, she came out all right and is a cheerful, busy little woman now.

And there was Humpy Bill as the folks called poor little Billy Jordan with the dreadful back so bent and bowed that his head leaned over and his eyes were always turned to the ground. He was real unhappy till it was put into my head to remind him how many things there was on the ground to look at and learn about and watch. As soon as he begun he went way beyond me. He learned all about the flowers and the grass and the flies and bees and bugs and caterpillars, even the stones themselves, and he got to be a happy, busy little chap, friends with everybody, not only folks but all creatures and to love them and Him too that made them all.

And there was John Long and his wife that got so far apart and worried me so till I found they really were dreadful fond of each other but had let things come between them. And of course, when I knew

that, I was able to bring them together—never mind how—without
their knowing I did it.   And—dear
me, I won't say another word.   I've
got to run in next door at three
o'clock to take care of little Reuben
while his mother goes to the doctor's.
He's a fretty, naughty little next-
door, but he likes me pretty well and
I can generally manage him.

AUNT
ABBY'S
FIRST
EASTER

I WASN'T brought up to keep Easter. To tell the truth, I didn't know anything about it, or what 'twas for, till I was a woman grown. You know there was a feeling, those days, against all such things, even Christmas itself, as Roman Catholic, or, anyway, Episcopal seasons, and not to be kept by other denominations. Why, pa used to tell how he sent a big, fat turkey, one time, on Christmas Day, to Parson Roe. The old man sent it back, with a note that said that any other day he'd take it, thankful, but not on a popish feast day. He didn't get turkey real often, neither, so it must have been hard work to return it.

So, as I said, I don't believe I'd ever heard of such a time as Easter till I was grown up. Then Dr. Watkins came to the village to practice, after old Dr. Ashby died. He was an Episcopal, and he wanted a church of that sort. He found a few other folks that felt the same way,—English Bill, the rope-maker, and Miss Viney Lee, whose father had been a Tory, and some young folks that wanted something new and queer,—and they started an Episcopal church. They used to have their meetings in a house way up at the north end of the village, not far from the burying-ground.

Well, I was spending the biggest part of my time, those days, in that burying-ground; for my little Danny, my only child, the only one I ever had, was laying there. I guess I've told you about him,—the cutest, prettiest little yellow-haired fellow, taken away from me so sudden, when he was hardly more than a baby. He died just at the beginning of winter. Maybe you know something about what that means. To lay down the little body you'd always kept so warm and careful, covering it with soft blankets, cuddling it close to you away from drafts or the least mite of cold air, holding its cunning little feet in your own warm hands, so's they'd never be chilled,—to lay down that soft, pretty baby, I say, in the cold, outdoors, and under the very snow itself,—oh, how can we ever, ever

bear to do it! But we have to,—so
many, many of us mothers have to.
It 'most broke my heart. I was a
member of the church, a believer,
and I tried to bear my trouble right.
I knew it was only the body, and
not the soul, that I was putting
away there. But I loved that little
body with all my heart and soul and
mind. In a mite of a child like
that, only going on two when he
died, it's the body part we love, almost more than the soul, seems to
me. The soul in a baby is so little
and hid up, you 'most overlook it.
I loved the yellow curly hair; the
blue eyes; the soft, pinky cheeks;
the little bit of a mouth, just as red
and sweet as one of my cinnamon
roses; the pretty baby fingers; the
helpless little feet,—every single

speck of that child's body that I'd held in my arms night and day for 'most twenty months. And now I must put it out in the cold, and leave it there. I tell you, even thinking of the happy little soul up in heaven didn't make up, just then, for losing and leaving all alone, out there, that blessed little body.

But I tried to take it right. I said, time and time again, from the very first, "Thy will be done." I told the Lord I knew it was all right, that He doeth all things well, that He only gave and took away again, and I said, over and over and over again, "Blessed be the name of the Lord." But as long as I felt that way,—didn't complain or rebel against God's will,—it didn't seem to me there was any harm in making much of that little bed where my baby's body laid. Seemed to me it was the best thing to do, making one think of God and His chastening, of heaven and the many mansions and the little children up there that always behold the face of their Father. So day after day, and week after week, I passed my time,—the biggest part of it,—there in the burying-ground, by Danny's little grave. I kept the snow away, and laid sweet-smelling fir balsam branches over it. Of course, there wasn't any flowers in bloom at that time of year, but I found pretty moss under the snow, and running pine, and I had everlastings, pearly white, that I'd picked and dried in the fall. So I kept that little bed sweet and pretty, and as warm as I

could. And there I sat hours and
hours of every day. I wrapped up
warm, so's not to take cold, and
somehow kept from getting real sick,
though I don't see now how it was.

Folks talked about it,—said they
never saw such sorrow, such mourning, in a mother before ; and somehow I liked to have them say it. I
liked to see them come to the windows as I went by in my gloomy
black clothes, with my white,
mournful face, and to know they
were saying, " Did you ever see such
a crushed, broken-hearted woman ?
Here it is two months, or more,
since her child was taken, and still
she just lives by his grave." You
know what I mean. I didn't do it
for that. I didn't even know I
liked to hear them talk that way,

but I see now that I did. I gave up
everything else for the sake of that
grave. I'd been interested in a good
many things before Danny died.
I'd belonged to the sewing society,
and was one of the busiest workers
in getting up the box of things we
sent off every year to the home mis-
sionaries out West. I had a class of
little boys in the Sabbath-school, and
I used to go out a good deal among
the poor and sick in the town. But
I gave all those things up now. It
would be too hard to make or mend
clothes for the missionary children
when my own little boy would never
need my sewing again. And how
could I talk to those boys in my
class, remembering my baby, who
would never grow up to be a little
lad like them! And I just could

not go out among the sick and
sorrowful, and try to comfort them,
when my own heart was sore and
aching, and 'most broke. I didn't
even go to meeting very often.
Wasn't the little grave a more
solemn, sacred spot than any earthly
temple? I said to myself. Wasn't
it good to be there,—better for my
poor hurt soul than all the preaching and hymn-singing, and that kind
of worship?

I don't see now how I could have
got so wrong and mistaken. There
was plenty of things to show me my
errors. Some one told me one day
that Eddie Freeman, one of my
Sabbath-school boys, was getting
into bad ways. He'd left the class
because he didn't like the new
teacher, and he was going with a

wild set of bigger boys, had learnt to swear and to do other bad things. "But my little boy is safe," I says to myself,—"safe here in his little quiet bed, with his mother watching over him day in and day out." There was a good deal of suffering that winter, sickness about and poverty. But hearing of it only made me keep closer to my grave, and think, "No sickness or sorrow can come here, to touch my baby in this blessed spot."

Well, it came spring. I was dreadful glad to see the first signs of it, the little pinky-white buds of the mayflower showing when you brushed the snow away, and the soft, furry mouse-ears peeking up at the foot of the trees. I picked all I could find of the earliest, weak, soft little blooms that made me think of my helpless little baby, and strimmered them all over his grave. I sowed some grass-seed there, and watched and watered it, and I loved that little heap, and stayed by it more and more, and forgot everything else in the whole world.

One Sunday in April I got up very early,—it wasn't quite light,— and started for the burying-ground. I'd found some white anemones the day before, and dug up a lot, and I wanted to set them out about my baby's bed. I didn't know it was anything particular that day, though I recollected it was the Sabbath. But I remember it was a beautiful morning, soft and bright, with a pinky light over everything as the sun came up. And somehow, as I got to the burying-ground and set down my basket of plants, there came into my mind the verse in the Bible about the women coming "very early in the morning at the rising of the sun" to the sepulchre of our Lord. And just then I heard music. It came from the building where the Episcopals held their meetings, right close to the burying-ground. 'Twas singing, and though it was soft and sweet, I could hear every word plain. The first thing that came to my ears was, "He is not here, not here; He is not here." I don't know myself why those words struck me so. They're in the Bible, and I'd read them dozens of times. Maybe it was because everything was so still, and I had thought I was all alone,

the only person awake in all the
place, but anyway those words
seemed to be spoke, or sung, to me
myself, and nobody else, and they
seemed to have a terrible meaning.
I started up, and I says to myself,—
I don't know but I said it out loud,
"Not here! the Lord is not *here!*"
And soft, soft, but real clear and
sweet, I heard the words again in a
sort of chant like, "He is not here,
not here. Why seek ye the living
among the dead?"

I dropped down again on the
ground by my baby's grave, and
covered up my eyes. In one quick
minute I seemed to see the truth, and
to know what I had been doing, and,
more, what I had been leaving un-
done. 'Twas just as if some big
stone had been rolled away that had

hid the truth, and I could see,—
could see something, but not all.
" Not here," I says to myself,—" not
where I have spent these long
months, not in this solemn place I've
set so much by and made so fair and
sweet. Then where, oh, just tell me,
where is the Lord? For you have
taken Him away, and I don't know
where you have laid Him." And the
sweet singing went on chanting-like
again, " He is risen, He is risen." I
looked up, way up, as far away from
that little heaped-up grave as I could
look, into the blue sky with the sort
of pinky light over it, and it seemed
so far away. I cried out, " Oh !
what shall I do?" And right away
I heard the voices chanting out the
answer, " Go, tell My brethren, Go,
quickly," they were singing, " Go,

tell My disciples." I understood.
How could I help it? What notice
had I taken of His disciples, His
brethren, all these last months?
They'd gone hungry, untaught, un-
comforted, for all me. And now,
oh! was it too late? And the voices
went on, " Behold, He goeth before
you into Galilee, there shall ye
see Him." And the tears—such
ashamed ones, but almost glad too,
as I heard those words, and felt there
was another chance for me yet—came
a-streaming down my face. I took
that chance. I say it very humbly.
I took up my work again, leaving
my Danny and his little grave to the
Lord's care. I learnt my boys in
Sabbath-school again, I worked for
the missionary box, I visited amongst
the poor and the sick and the sorry,

and I can tell you, very humbly, as I said before, but very thankful, in the Bible words, as I " went to tell His disciples, behold, Jesus met " me.

I found afterwards it was Easter Sunday, and I learnt all about the day and what 'twas kept for, and, Congregational as I am, you know, I've kept it ever since. I found out too that the singing that morning was the children chanting, as they call it, the story of that first rising, the Lord's resurrection. It wasn't the regular anthem the Episcopals use that day, but one the minister had got up and learnt them, and they were using that day for the first time. Do you think I don't know why they were led to sing it that morning? Do you think I hold that it only just happened so?

AUNT ABBY'S
PASTURE
WITH A ROCK
IN IT

IX AUNT ABBY'S PASTURE WITH A ROCK IN IT

NO, I don't go away summers. Oh, yes, I know; most folks do, the best of folks,—ministers and all. And they tell me I'd ought to go; say it's refreshing and wakening and lifting and broadening. The church at the Hollow, and the one at the East road, and Mr. Edwards's, all shut up for three weeks at a time in warm weather; and we don't have any Sunday-school at all nowadays in July and August.

Mr. Edwards says he gets more strength of body and mind, more help for his work and points for his sermons, in his vacation at the sea-

shore or the mountains than in all
the year besides. I dare say. But I
don't exactly see my way to going;
there are things to see to here, and
it costs something even at the
cheapest places. And I've got a
way of my own of having a vacation. I don't know but after all I'm
lifted and broadened and strength-
ened as much, and get as many
points out of it, as the rest with all
their travelling. Maybe you'll smile
when I tell you where I go, and
what kind of a place it is. It's
nothing in the world but a pasture
with a rock in it.

It isn't half a mile from my house,
though I'm right in the busiest part
of Factoryville, you know. You go
down to the bobbin-mill, and then
along north as far as Giles's store;

then you turn to the left, and keep
right straight ahead. And there
'tis,—a good bit of pasture-land, and
a big bowlder about the middle of it.

I came upon it two years ago. I
hadn't lived here long, and wasn't
used to a big, bustling town like
this; and when hot weather came I
did just ache for fresh air and growing things and woodsy places.

I went out one day, and walked
and walked, trying to find big trees
and bushes and such things. By
and by I saw something green
ahead, and 'twas this. I stopped at
the rail fence, and looked over.
Just at first it didn't seem very in-
viting when I thought of the woods
at my old home, all dark and cool,
with soft, wet moss for your feet to
step on, and brooks running along;

and I says to myself, but out loud,
" It's nothing in the world but a
pasture with a rock in it."

Well, do you know I hadn't more
than spoke those words than I
seemed to see a wonderful meaning
in them. I forgot all about the heat
and the dusty road, and I crawled
through the rails and went over to
the bowlder and sat down on the
grass, and I began to think.
" Why," I went on to myself,
" what's religion when you think of
it, or, come to that, what's heaven
itself, any more than that,—a pasture with a rock in it ? " I began to
love that place right then and there.
I can't tell you what it's been to me,
and all the thinking and help and
brand-new light I've found there.
Points for sermons ! Why it's just

bristly with them. I find a fresh one every time I go, and I haven't near come to the end yet.

Some days I'll be so tired I can't do a mortal thing but just stretch myself full length out on the grass and keep still, and then'll come into my head that verse out of mother's favorite psalm—I guess 'twas your mother's too, 'tis most folks's mother's—about "He maketh me to lie down in green pastures." Deary me! I don't want a better sermon; and again I'll get to looking at the grass. There's red-top, and timothy, and a little herd's grass there, and it looks so pretty shaking in the wind. And I recollect how our Lord took notice of all such little things. "If God so clothe the grass of the field," you know; and, before I know it, that's led me off into the most comforting, beautiful thinking.

And then there's the rock; I can't hardly talk much about that, but you know what I mean. " Green fields beyond the swelling flood," as mother used to sing, is all sightly and beautiful; but, after all, it's the Rock up there that's such a thing to lean on and look to. And down here in this world, too, lying down in green pastures and watching the grass, is nice and comforting in fair days; but come to storms and rough weather, a rock is what we want the most after all.

I believe I get more points out of that bowlder than I do out of the pasture. In a hot afternoon I get on the east side of it in the shade, and then I think of the " man that shall

be the shadow of a great rock in
a weary land." Sometimes there
comes up a storm with such pouring
rain, and I creep under the lee of
that bowlder, and keep safe and dry.
And then I'm sure to get thinking
of the "strong rock for a house of
defense," and of father's hymn,

> " Rock of ages, cleft for me,
>   Let me hide myself in thee."

Sometimes it's Moses hiding away
in the rock to watch the Lord pass
by; again it's the rod bringing
water out of the rock; and lots of
times it's about that tomb hewn out
of a rock, that new sepulchre in a
garden wherein was never man yet
laid. Or by spells I think of David
keeping his father's sheep, and lead-
ing them out in the pastures; or
Isaac going out into the fields at

eventide, and that beautiful story of
the shepherds abiding in the fields
around Bethlehem.

But after all, I come back most
times to the thing itself, just as it
struck me the first time I ever saw
it,—a pasture with a rock in it. So
I don't go away in warm weather,
and I never expect to now. For I'm
getting on in years, and there's
plenty of things in my own little
watering-place here to last as long as
I shall for points to think about, and
for strengthening and lifting and
widening. It won't be long, at the
most, before I go away for good
some summer. I shall be satisfied
when I wake up there; but I can't
help hoping the place will be a little
like a pasture, and I'm certain sure
there'll be a Rock in it.